Arranged for *all* electronic keyboards *by Kenneth Baker.*

THE COMPL
KEYBOARD PL   R

90s LOVE SONGS

Wise Publications
London/New York/Paris/Sydney/Copenhagen/Madrid

Exclusive Distributors:
Music Sales Limited
8/9 Frith Street, London W1V 5TZ, England.
Music Sales Pty Limited
120 Rothschild Avenue, Rosebery, NSW 2018, Australia.

This book © Copyright 1999 by
Wise Publications
Order No. AM952655
ISBN 0-7119-7412-8

Compiled by Peter Evans
Music arranged by Kenneth Baker
Music processed by Dakota Music Service

Cover photograph courtesy of Super Stock

Your Guarantee of Quality
As publishers, we strive to produce every book
to the highest commercial standards.
The music has been freshly engraved and the book has been
carefully designed to minimise awkward page turns and to make
playing from it a real pleasure.
Particular care has been given to specifying acid-free, neutral-sized paper
made from pulps which have not been elemental chlorine bleached.
This pulp is from farmed sustainable forests and was produced with special
regard for the environment. Throughout, the printing and binding have been
planned to ensure a sturdy, attractive publication which should give years of enjoyment.
If your copy fails to meet our high standards, please inform us and
we will gladly replace it.

Music Sales' complete catalogue describes thousands of titles and is available in
full colour sections by subject, direct from Music Sales Limited.
Please state your areas of interest and send a cheque/postal order for £1.50 for postage to:
Music Sales Limited, Newmarket Road, Bury St. Edmunds, Suffolk IP33 3YB.

www.internetmusicshop.com

Printed in the United Kingdom by
Printwise (Haverhill) Limited, Suffolk.

LOOKING FOR LOVE

Words & Music by Ben Watt & Tracey Thorn

Voice: flute
Rhythm: 8 beat
Tempo: medium (♩=128)

VERSES

1. I was a-lone, thinkin' I was just fine I wasn't lookin' for a-ny-one to be mine. I thought love was just a fab-ri-ca-tion, a train that wouldn't stop at my sta-tion. Home a-lone, that was my con-sign-ment, so-li-ta-ry con-fine-ment. So when we met I was skirtin' a-round you, I didn't know I was lookin' for love un-til I found you.

2. Coz there you stood, and I would, or I won-dered. Could I say how I felt and not be mis-un-der-stood. A thou-sand stars came in-to my sy-stem. I ne-ver knew how much I had missed them. Slap up-on the mat of my heart you land-ed, I was coy with you and you were can-did. And now the plan-ets cir-cle a-round you. I didn't know I was lookin' for love un-til I

add horn

CHORUS

4

WHAT CAN I DO

Words & Music by Andrea Corr, Caroline Corr, Sharon Corr & Jim Corr

Voice: vibraphone
Rhythm: rock
Tempo: fairly slow (♩=80)

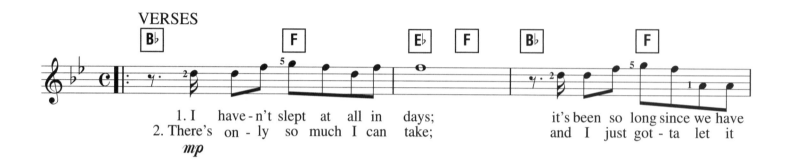

1. I have-n't slept at all in days;   it's been so long since we have
2. There's on-ly so much I can take;   and I just got-ta let it

talked.   And I have been here ma-ny times;
go.   And who knows, I might feel bet - ter,

I just don't know what I'm do-in' wrong.
if I don't cry, and I don't hope.

What can I do to make you

love me?   What can I do to make you care?

YOU'RE STILL THE ONE

Words & Music by Shania Twain & Robert John "Mutt" Lange

Voice: electronic organ
Rhythm: pop rock
Tempo: quite fast (♩=138)

We're still to-geth - er,____ still go - ing____ strong. (Still the one!) You're still the one I run ____ to,____ the one that I be - long____ to.____ You're still the one I want____ for life. (Still the one!) You're still the one that I____ love,____ the on-ly one I dream____ of____ You're still the one I kiss____ ____ good - night.____

cresc.

CHORUS

to e. organ trio

D.S. and fade for ending

to guitar

WHEN I NEED YOU

Words & Music by Albert Hammond & Carole Bayer Sager

Voice: harp
Rhythm: 6/8 blues (or slow rock)
Tempo: slow 2 (♩ = 50)

BRIDGE

harp to flute

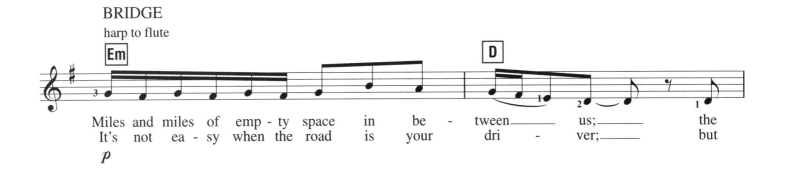

Miles and miles of emp - ty space in be - tween_____ us;_____ the
It's not ea - sy when the road is your dri - ver;_____ but

p

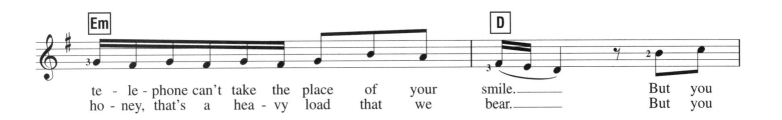

te - le - phone can't take the place of your smile._____ But you
ho - ney, that's a hea - vy load that we bear._____ But you

know I won't be tra - vel - ling for - e - ver;_____ it's cold out, but hold out, and
know I won't be tra - vel - ling a life - time_____ it's cold out, but hold out, and

cresc.   *f*

1.   flute to harp   2.
do   like   I   do. 2. When   I   do   like   I   do. Oh   I

mp

INSTRUMENTAL

Flute to Piano

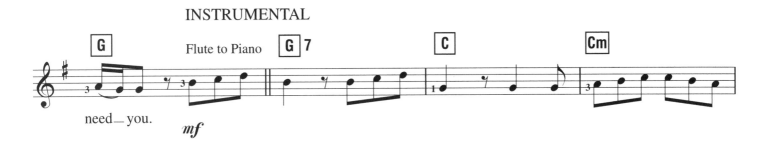

need__ you.   *mf*

D.S. and fade ad. lib.

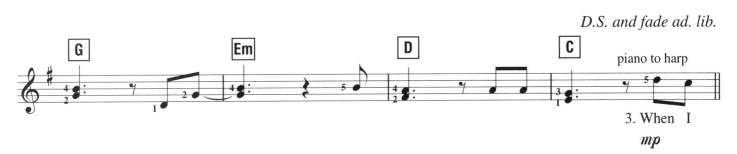

piano to harp

3. When   I

mp

11

ALL I HAVE TO GIVE

Words & Music by Full Force

Voice: piano
Rhythm: 8 beat
Tempo: medium (♩=96)

CAN YOU FEEL THE LOVE TONIGHT?

(FROM WALT DISNEY PICTURES' "THE LION KING")

As performed by Elton John

Music by Elton John. Lyrics by Tim Rice

Voice: oboe
Rhythm: 8 beat
Tempo: fairly slow (♩=72)

It's e-nough for this wide— eyed— wan-der-er—

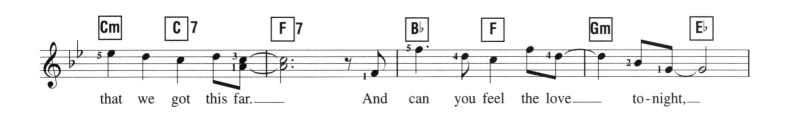

that we got this far.— And can you feel the love— to-night,—

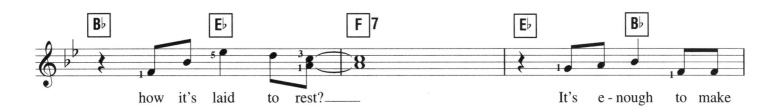

how it's laid to rest?— It's e-nough to make

cut strings   *To Coda*

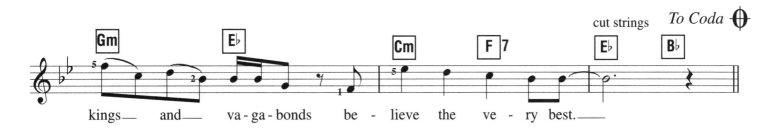

kings— and— va-ga-bonds be - lieve the ve-ry best.—

INSTRUMENTAL

D.C al Coda

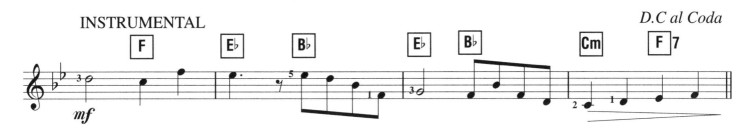

mf

CODA

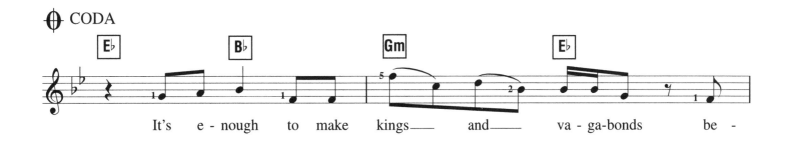

It's e - nough to make kings— and— va-ga-bonds be -

stop rhythm

lieve the ve - ry best.—

LIFTED

Words & Music by Paul Tucker, Emmanuel Baiyewu & Martin Brammer

Voice: clarinet
Rhythm: rock
Tempo: medium (♩=102)

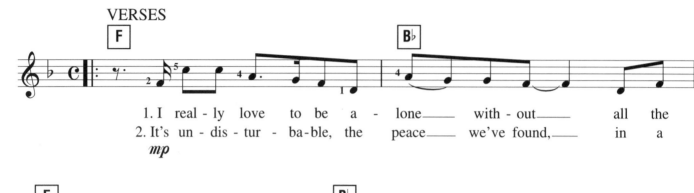

1. I real - ly love to be a - lone____ with - out____ all the
2. It's un - dis - tur - ba - ble, the peace____ we've found,____ in a

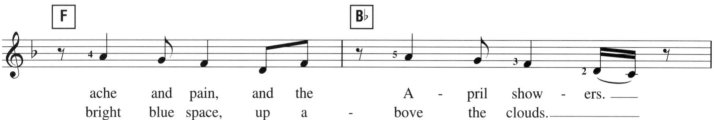

ache and pain, and the A - pril show - ers. ____
bright blue space, up a - bove the clouds. ____

But it ain't long be - fore I long____ for you____ like a
Where ev - 'ry - thing is un - der - stand____ a - ble,____ you don't

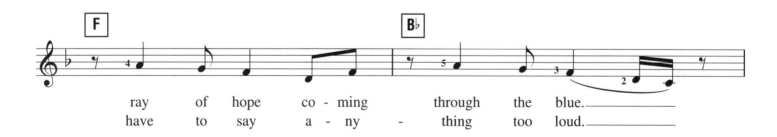

ray of hope co - ming through the blue. ____
have to say a - ny - thing too loud. ____

When it all gets dark and then the whole thing falls a - part, I guess it
When our luck runs out,____ and we're brought back down to so - lid ground, I

MISSING

Music by Ben Watt. Words by Tracey Thorn

Voice: human voice
Rhythm: 8 beat
Tempo: medium (♩=128)

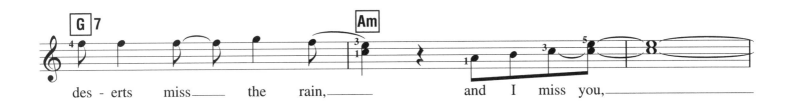

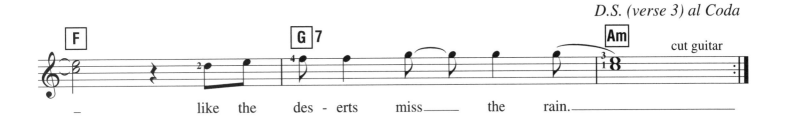

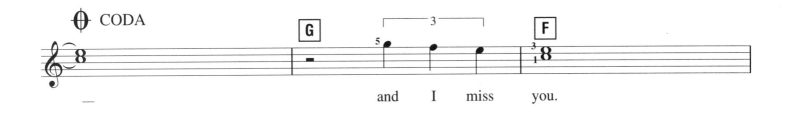

I LOVE THE WAY YOU LOVE ME

Words & Music by Chuck Cannon & Victoria Shaw

Voice: string ensemble
Rhythm: 8 beat
Tempo: slow (♩=84)

VERSES

1. I like the feel___ of your name on my lips, ___ and
(2.) I like the way___ your eyes dance when you laugh, ___ and

mp

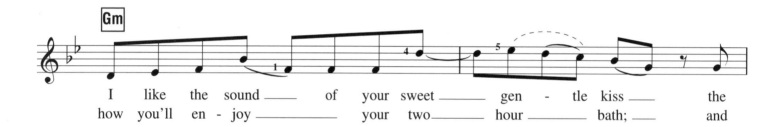

I like the sound ___ of your sweet ___ gen - tle kiss ___ the
how you'll en - joy ___ your two ___ hour ___ bath; ___ and

way that your fin - gers run ___ through my ___ hair, ___ and
how you con-vinced ___ me to dance in the ___ rain, ___ with

cresc.

how your scent lin - gers, e - ven when you're not ___ there ___ 2. And
ev - 'ry - one watch - in', like we

mf *mp*

CHORUS

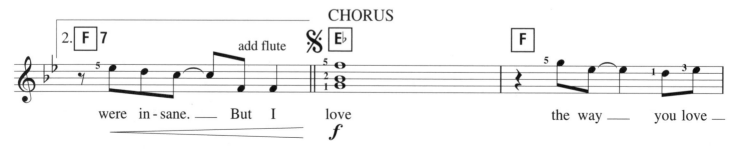

add flute

were in - sane. ___ But I love the way ___ you love ___

f

HIGH

Music by Paul Tucker & Tunde Baiyewu. Words by Paul Tucker

Voice: saxophone
Rhythm: rock
Tempo: medium (♩=104)

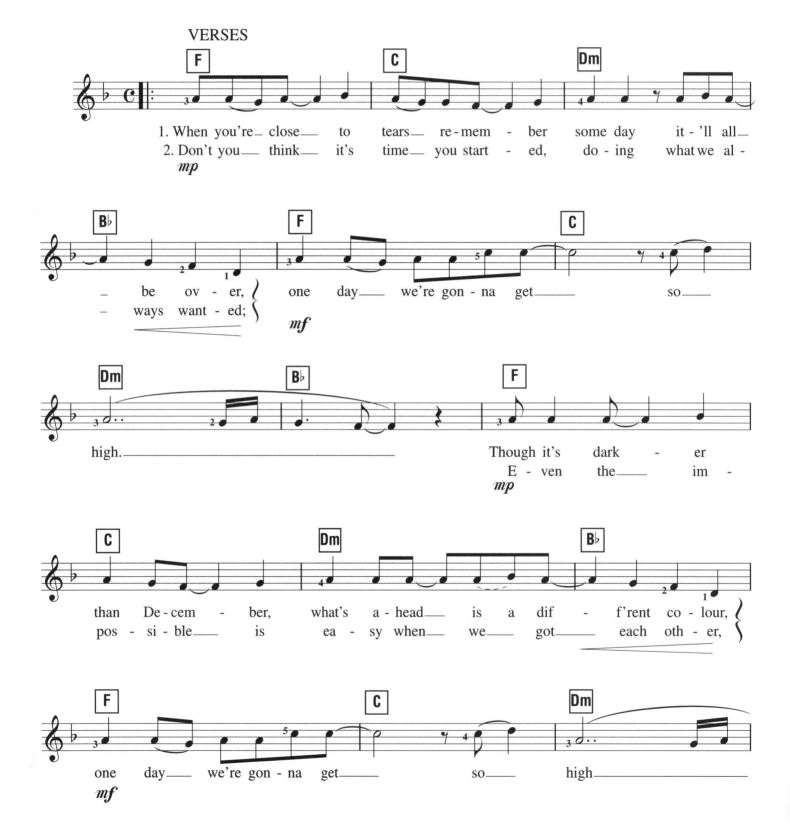

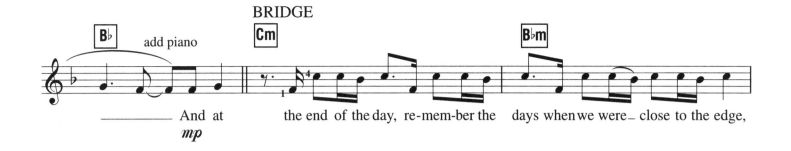

BRIDGE

And at the end of the day, re-mem-ber the days when we were close to the edge,

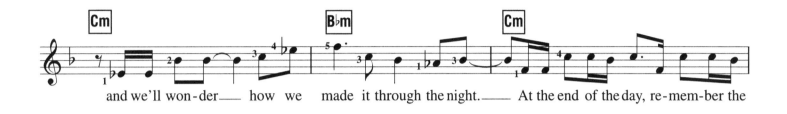

and we'll won-der how we made it through the night. At the end of the day, re-mem-ber the

way we stayed so close to the end, but re-mem-ber it was me and you. 'Cause

cresc

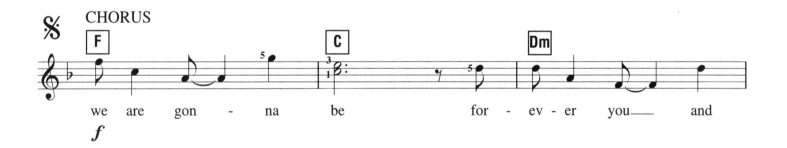

CHORUS

we are gon - na be for - ev - er you and

f

me. You will al - ways keep me fly - ing high in the

D.S. and fade ad lib.

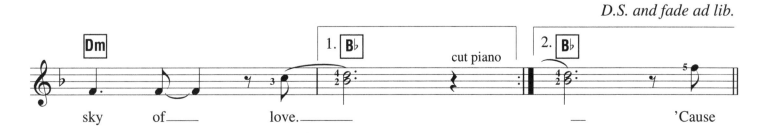

sky of love. 'Cause

MY ALL

Music by Mariah Carey & Walter Afanasieff. Words by Mariah Carey

Voice: clarinet
Rhythm: 8 beat
Tempo: slow (♩=54)

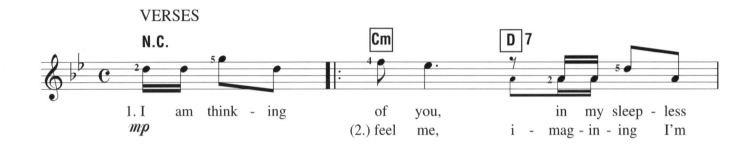

VERSES

1. I am think-ing of you, in my sleep-less
(2.) feel me, i-mag-in-ing I'm

so-li-tude to-night. If it's wrong to love you, then my heart just
look-ing in your eyes. I can see you clear-ly vi-vid-ly em-

won't let me be right, 'cause I've drowned in you, and I won't pull through with-out you by my
bla-zoned in my mind. And you're just so far, like a dis-tant star I'm wish-ing on to-

CHORUS
add flute

side. I'd give my all to have just
night.

one more night with you; I'd risk my life to feel your

bo - dy next to mine; 'cause I can't__ go on__ liv-ing in the

To Coda ⊕

mem - 'ry of our song. I'd__ give my all__ for your love to -

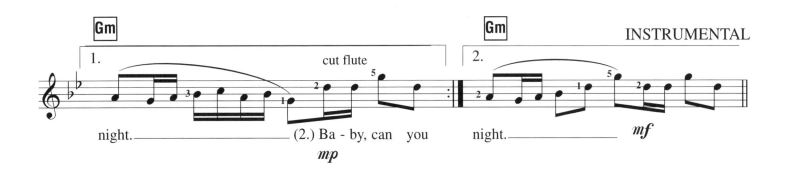

INSTRUMENTAL

1. cut flute 2.

night.__ (2.) Ba - by, can you night.__ *mf*
mp

Ooh,__

⊕ CODA *Rit.*

D.S. al Coda stop rhythm

nah.__ I'd give my night.__

YOU'RE GORGEOUS

Words & Music by Stephen Jones

Voice: marimba (or steel band)
Rhythm: reggae 16
Tempo: medium (♩=126)

you're _____ gor - geous, I know you'll get ____ me through.

VERSES

cut brass

_____

3. You said my clothes were se - xy, ____

4. You said I was - n't cheap, _____

mf

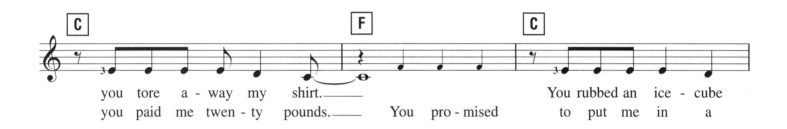

you tore a - way my shirt. ____ You rubbed an ice - cube

you paid me twen - ty pounds. ____ You pro - mised to put me in a

(TO CHORUS)

1. add brass

on my chest, ____ snapped me till it hurt. ____ Be - cause

ma - ga - zine ____ on ev - 'ry ta - ble in ev - 'ry lounge.

f

INSTRUMENTAL

2. add brass

f

D.S. and fade on CHORUS

1. 2.

GIVE ME A LITTLE MORE TIME

Words & Music by Gabrielle, Andy Dean, Benjamin Wolf & Ben Barson

Voice: saxophone
Rhythm: 8 beat
Tempo: medium (♩=114)

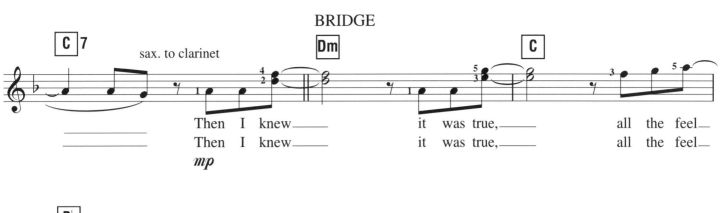

BRIDGE

sax. to clarinet

Then I knew_____ it was true,_____ all the feel_
Then I knew_____ it was true,_____ all the feel_

mp

_ ings I had_____ in - side for you. I could not de - ny,_____
_ ings that you had, I shared them too. I could not de - ny,_____

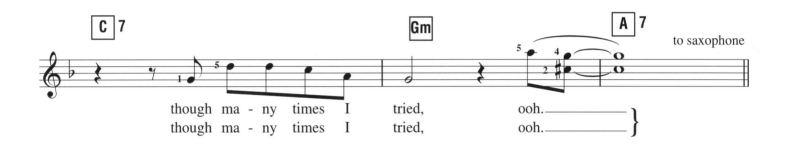

to saxophone

though ma - ny times I tried, ooh._____
though ma - ny times I tried, ooh._____ }

CHORUS

Give me a li - tle more time,_____ I need to make up my mind,_____ 'Cause you know_

f

_ I'm in_ two minds,_____ I wan-na be more than your friend,_____ oh I just can't pre-tend_

D.C. (Verse 2)

Repeat chorus & fade for ending

_ a - ny long - er; feel - ings get-ting strong-er._____ - ings get-ting strong-er.

KISS THE GIRL

Words & Howard Ashman. Music by Alan Menken

Voice: piano + vibraphone
Rhythm: reggae 16
Tempo: slow (♩.=64)
       (double time feel)

VERSES

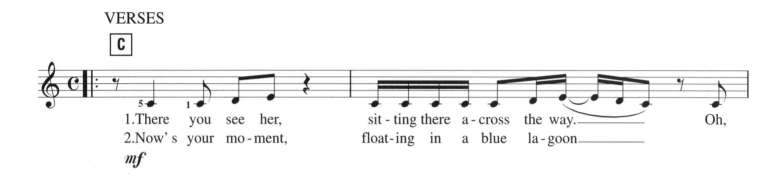

1.There you see her, sit - ting there a - cross the way.___ Oh,
2.Now's your mo - ment, float-ing in a blue la - goon___

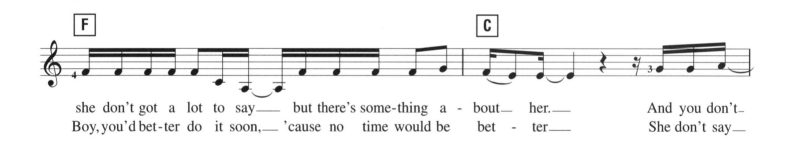

she don't got a lot to say___ but there's some-thing a - bout___ her.___ And you don't_
Boy, you'd bet-ter do it soon,___ 'cause no time would be bet - ter___ She don't say_

_ know why,___ but you're dy - ing to try,___ you wan - na kiss the girl.
_ a word,___ and she won't_ say a word___ un - til you kiss the girl.

Yes, you want_ her,___ look at her you know you do.___

Pos - si - ble she wants you to,__ but there's one__ way to ask__ her.__ It don't take__

__ a word,__ not a sin - gle word, go on and kiss the girl.

add flute

𝄋 CHORUS

1. (Sha la la la la la) My, oh my,__ Look like the boy too shy,_ Ain't gon - na__ kiss the girl.__
2. (Sha la la la la la) Don't be scared, you got the mood pre - pared, go on and__ kiss the girl.__

f

cut flute

(Sha la la la la la) ain't that sad, _ Ain't it a shame, too bad,__ He gon - na__ miss the girl.
(Sha la la la la la) Don't stop now,_ don't try to hide it, how__ you wan - na__ kiss the girl.

D.S. and fade for ending

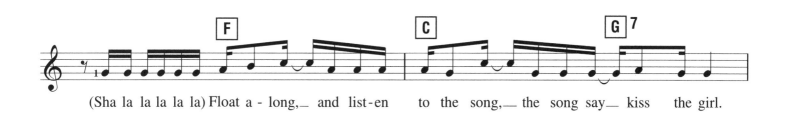

(Sha la la la la la) Float a - long,__ and list-en to the song,__ the song say__ kiss the girl.

(Sha la la la la) the mu - sic play,__ do what the mu - sic say,__ you got - ta kiss the girl.__

STRANDED

Words & Music by Larossi, Rami Yacoub & Daniel Papalexis

Voice: harp
Rhythm: 8 beat
Tempo: medium (♩=92)

CHORUS

I don't wa-na feel like I'm strand-ed,_____ Oh, ba-by,

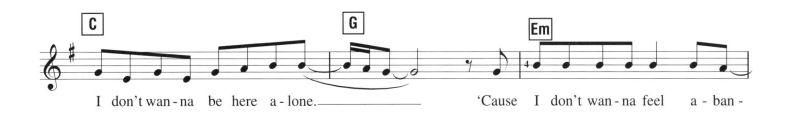

I don't wan-na be here a-lone._____ 'Cause I don't wan-na feel a-ban-

- doned,_____ but may-be heav-en is the place our love be-longs._____

INTERLUDE

I'll know I'll see you a-gain_____ some day.   I'll be   wait-ing for that day all my life._____

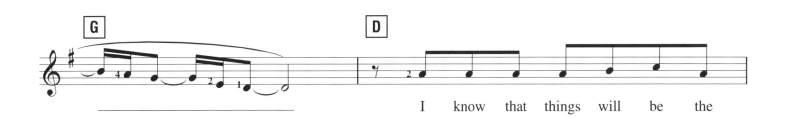

I   know   that   things   will   be   the

D.S. (fade ad lib.)

same a - gain,_____ I know some-day I'll see you a - gain_____

ALWAYS

Words & Music by Jon Bon Jovi

Voice: guitar
Rhythm: 8 beat
Tempo: slow (♩=72)

SOMETHING CHANGED

Music by Pulp. Lyrics by Jarvis Cocker

Voice: piano
Rhythm: rock
Tempo: medium ($\quarternote$=124)

VERSES

1. I wrote this song_____ two hours be-fore we met._____
2. Do you be-lieve_____ there's some-one up a-bove?_____

mp

— I did-n't know_____ your name, or
— Does he have a time - ta-ble, dir -

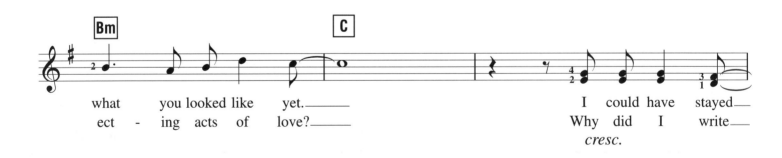

what you looked like yet._____ I could have stayed_____
ect - ing acts of love?_____ Why did I write_____

cresc.

— at home, and gone_____ to bed.
— this song on that_____ one day?_____

mf

I could have gone___ to see a film___ in - stead,___
Why did you touch___ my hand, and soft - ly say?___

mp cresc.   *mf*

___ you might have changed___ your mind, and___
___ Stop ask - ing ques - tions that don't___

seen___ your friends.___   Life
mat - ter an - y - way.___   Just

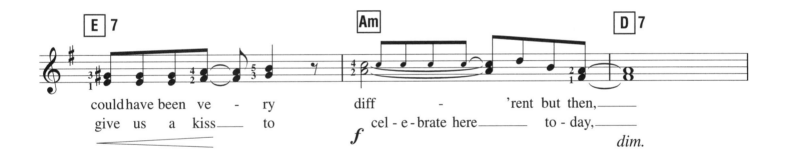

could have been ve - ry diff - 'rent but then,___
give us a kiss___ to cel - e - brate here___ to - day,___

f   *dim.*

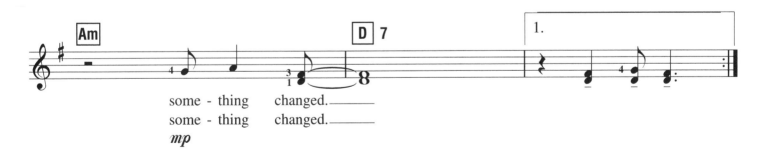

1.

some - thing changed.___
some - thing changed.___

mp

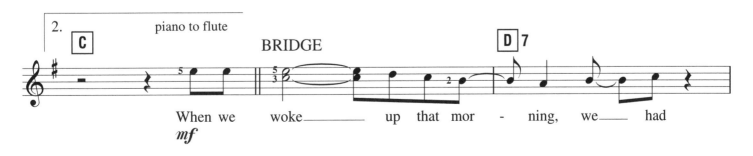

2.   piano to flute

BRIDGE

When we woke___ up that mor - ning, we___ had

mf

no———— way of know - ing that in a mat - - ter of ho -

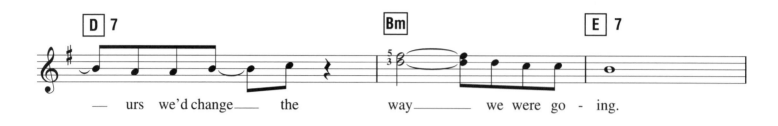

— urs we'd change——— the way——— we were go - ing.

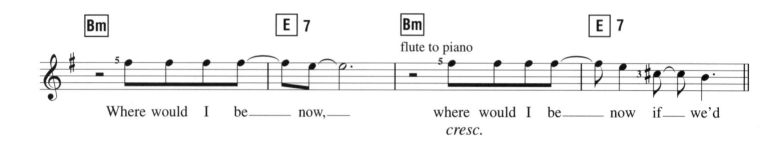

Where would I be——— now,——— where would I be——— now if—— we'd

cresc.

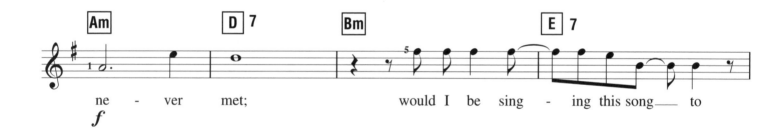

ne - ver met; would I be sing - ing this song—— to

f

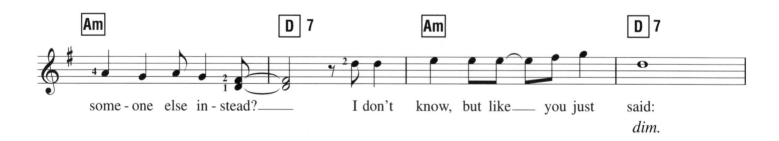

some - one else in - stead?——— I don't know, but like—— you just said:

dim.

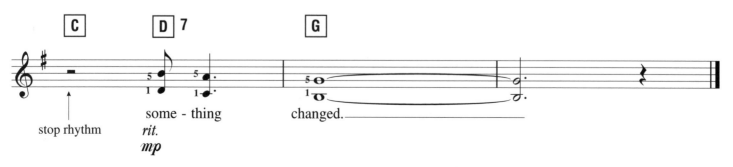

some - thing changed.———————————

stop rhythm   *rit.*

mp

38

CHORD CHARTS (For Left Hand)

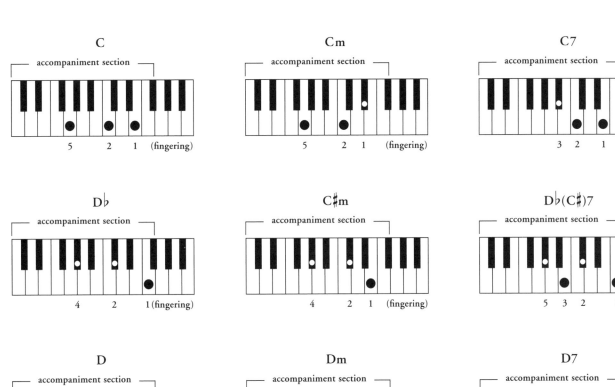
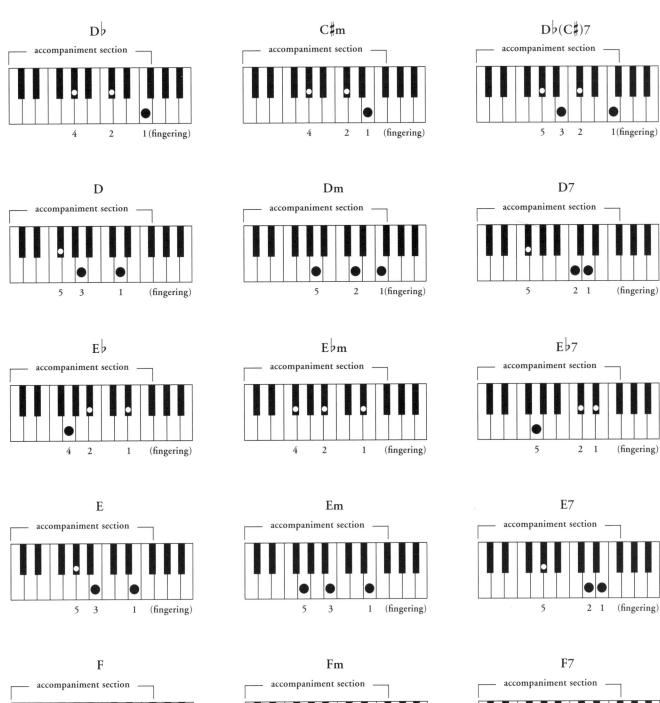
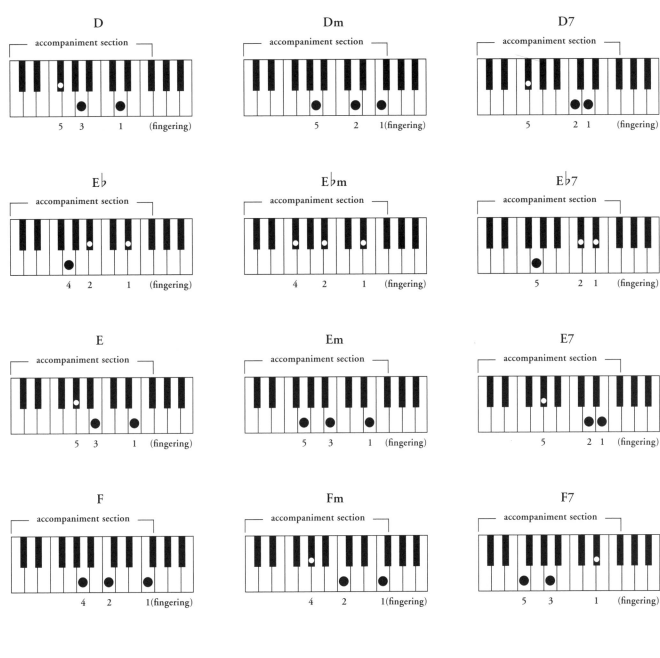
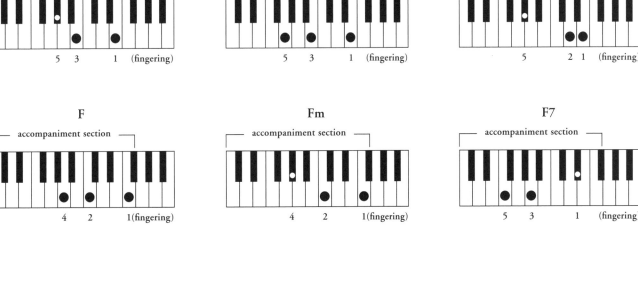

CHORD CHARTS (For Left Hand)

G♭(F♯)
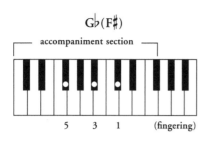

F♯m
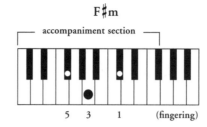

G♭(F♯)7
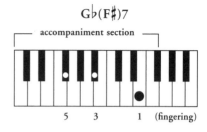

G
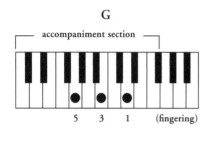

Gm
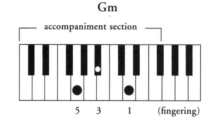

G7
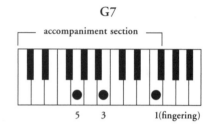

A♭
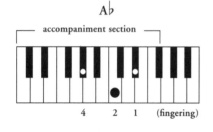

A♭m
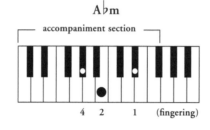

A♭7
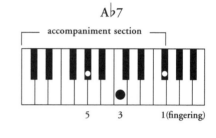

A
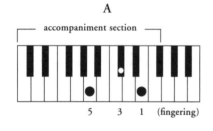

Am
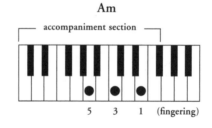

A7
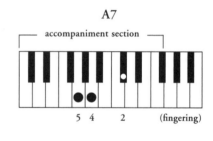

B♭
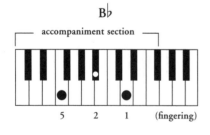

B♭m
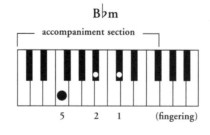

B♭7
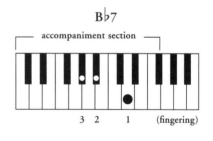

B
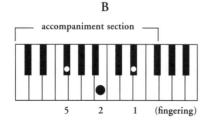

Bm
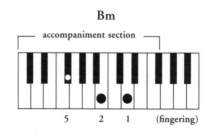

B7
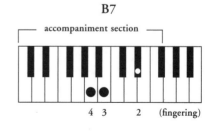

10/01 (41535)